Usborne

First Colouring Superheroes

Illustrated by Jenny Brown

Words by Kate Nolan

Let's go, Skydart!

Where's your next mission, Cloud Speeder?

Frostblast...

...and
Fireflinger.
What a team!

Hey, Doom Dragon! Over here!

Uh-oh... I'll never
beat Starflow!

CRASH!
Lightning Bolt's
power is AWESOME.

VROOOM! I'm Whizz.
Do you like my supercar?

Another day saving
the world - good job,
Captain Shield!

Professor Bloom
fights the Fang
Flower.

Lightgleam brings peace to the planet.

I'm Stella Storm - reporting back to Superhero HQ.

ZZZZING!
Go, Laser Blazer!

Hoverex
LOVES his
scooter.

BOOM! Sound Wave
strikes again!

Windshock - on the lookout
for his next mission

Alien attack?
No problem for
Atomic Alexa!

A superhero
helmet and
super-boots

A top-secret space
adventure for Cosmic Cal

Here comes
the Defender!

Aquanella to
the rescue!

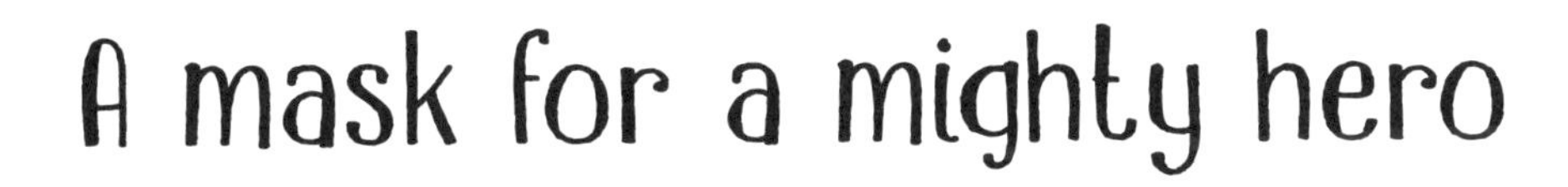

A mask for a mighty hero

The city needs you,
Blaze Beam! POW!

Stomp, stomp,
STOMP!

Helpstar - always
here to save the day

I'm Jet Dash
and my boots
are GREAT.

Zap defeats the
Mega-Monster!

I'm Glider. Flying is FUN!

SWOOSH!
Tsunami Kid holds
back the waves.

Earth, we have a problem... we need you, Rocket Force!

Protectro is home at last.
That was a long day!